SPIRIT ANIMA

COLOURING BOOK

SARAH WILDER

HAY HOUSE

Carlsbad, California • New York City • London
Sydney • Johannesburg • Vancouver • New Delhi

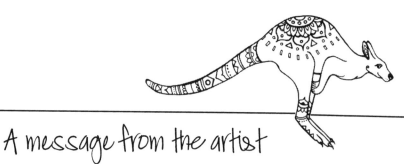

A message from the artist

Working with animal magic has been something I have intuitively done since I was a little girl. Looking back at my childhood photographs, you rarely see me without a dog, cat, chicken or some form of wildlife.

As a young adult, I followed two very different careers: fashion design and animal husbandry. My ego called me to fashion, but my soul called me to work with animals. I spent my time balancing both for many years, yo-yoing from studying clothing production to native animal rehabilitation. On weekends, I would spend one day sewing and designing, the next volunteering at the Australia Zoo wildlife hospital. After a while, I ended up finding more financial success and opportunity in fashion, so I chose to put the animal career goals on hold.

I still feel a deep connection to animals; they make me happy and peaceful. I'm instinctively drawn to them and I have such a profound respect for them and their gifts. The term for my passion and intuitive connection to animals is 'Zoomancy'. This is the art of divination or intuitive insight, based on the observation of animals. I believe that everyone has the ability to be a Zoomancer. It is something we don't have to learn; it is within us all, if we are so inclined.

This book is my opportunity to show animals my gratitude and hopefully inspire others to do a bit of inner work and reconnect with the non-human spirits that share this earth with us. This is our chance to visit the places where our instincts and intuitive voices lie, using stunning imagery and familiar animal figures to guide us.

Introduction to mandalas

Pronounced *MUN-DAH-LAH*, this beautiful form of self-expression originates from a Sanskrit word meaning 'circle' or 'centre'. Mandalas are embraced by many cultures, who use different methods to interpret this art form (sand, medicine wheels, architecture and art). However, the essence and meaning is always the same, with mandalas representing wholeness, unity, healing and harmony.

Mandalas are not just another form of art. They are also used in conjunction with healing, meditation, reflection, relaxation, balance, reconnection, mindfulness and as a form of medicine.

As circles and spirals make up so much of our own environment, it is no wonder we feel a connection to mandalas. The sun, moon and planets are all circular and we refer to our friends, family and community as 'circles'—all equal, all one, with no beginning or end. We have a subconscious love for mandalas because we are genetically, scientifically and spiritually connected to them. Now we are starting to connect with them consciously too.

Choosing an image

Just select an animal you feel connected to on a particular day, or make a selection based on a word you want to bring attention to in your life. Flip through the pages until you feel called by a particular animal, or head to the list on the next page and select a word you wish to focus on.

Choosing colours

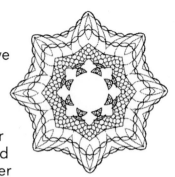

There are two approaches you can take to choosing the colours for your creative meditation mandalas:

Intuitive selection—an organic approach which honours your inner flow, starting the colouring process with little thought or planning. This is ideal for anyone wanting to uncover some subconscious feelings through colour therapy. After completing your artwork, you are encouraged to meditate on the colours and design (perhaps refer to a colour meaning chart), to uncover some of the inner feelings that may have surfaced during your meditation.

Intentional selection—use this approach when you are seeking a specific outcome, whether it be to promote healing, unlock your creativity or inject some motivation and passion into your life.

Tips for colouring

- Contrast is important—colour extremes add drama and complement one another!
- Keep some white space to help bring the detail and colours out in your design.
- Start from the inside out to prevent smudging your work and help you to see which colour to use next.
- A well-lit, quiet space free of clutter is recommended.
- Meditation music (or a peaceful soundtrack) helps to avoid distraction.

A
Abundance: Pig, 67; Rabbit, 69; Turkey, 85
Action: Lionfish, 50
Adaptation / Adaptability / Adaptable: Clownfish, 16; Fox, 34; Pig, 67
Advantage: Giraffe, 37
Adventure: Komodo Dragon, 48
Angels: Bluebird, 7
Authenticity: Parrotfish, 62
Awareness: Moth, 58

B
Balance: Kangaroo, 44; Magpie, 55; Zebra, 91
Beauty: Lady Beetle, 49
Bravery: Koi, 47

C
Celebration: Camel, 10; Parrotfish, 62
Change: Butterfly, 9
Cleanse: Frog, 35
Clever: Fox, 34
Commitment: Bee, 5
Communication: Toucan, 84
Community: Ant, 2; Flamingo, 33
Compassion: Elephant, 31
Confidence: Bear, 4; Lion, 51; Toucan, 84
Connection: Elephant, 31; Hawk, 38; Kangaroo, 44; Wolf, 89

Contentment: Iguana, 41; Tortoise, 83
Co-operation: Dolphin, 25
Courage: Parrotfish, 62; Tiger, 82
Creation / Creativity / Creative Expression: Bowerbird, 8; Cockatoo, 17; Orangutan, 60; Spider, 77
Curiosity: Alpaca, 1
Cycles: Cicada, 15; Crab, 20

D
Defensive: Magpie, 55
Depth: Whale Shark, 88
Desire: Eel, 30
Discernment: Moose, 57
Divinity: Cat, 12; Unicorn, 87
Dreams / Dream Weaver: Bat, 3; Spider, 77
Drive: Eel, 30; Horse, 39

E
Emotional Strength: Lionfish, 50
Enchantment: Butterfly, 9
Endurance: Camel, 10
Energy: Chameleon, 14
Evolution: Snail, 75

F
Family: Gouldian Finch, 32; Macaw, 54
Femininity: Cow, 18
Flow: Jellyfish, 43
Focus: Hawk, 38; Rooster, 70

Freedom: Cockatoo, 17; Horse, 39
Friendship: Gouldian Finch, 32; Flamingo, 33

G
Gateway: Crow, 23
Gifts: Lionfish, 50
Goals: Komodo Dragon, 48
Good Luck / Luck: Bee, 5; Cricket, 21; Lady Beetle, 49
Grace: Deer, 24
Gratefulness: Turkey, 85
Growth: Caterpillar, 13
Guidance: Hawk, 38

H
Happiness: Bluebird, 7
Harmony: Swan, 81; Zebra, 91
Healing: Frog, 35
Home: Macaw, 54
Honesty: Rooster, 70
Honour: Turkey, 85

I
Illumination: Hummingbird, 40
Imagination: Dragonfly, 27
Impulse: Eel, 30
Individualism: Mandarin Fish, 56; Wolf, 89
Influence: Chameleon, 14; Toucan, 84

BAT

3

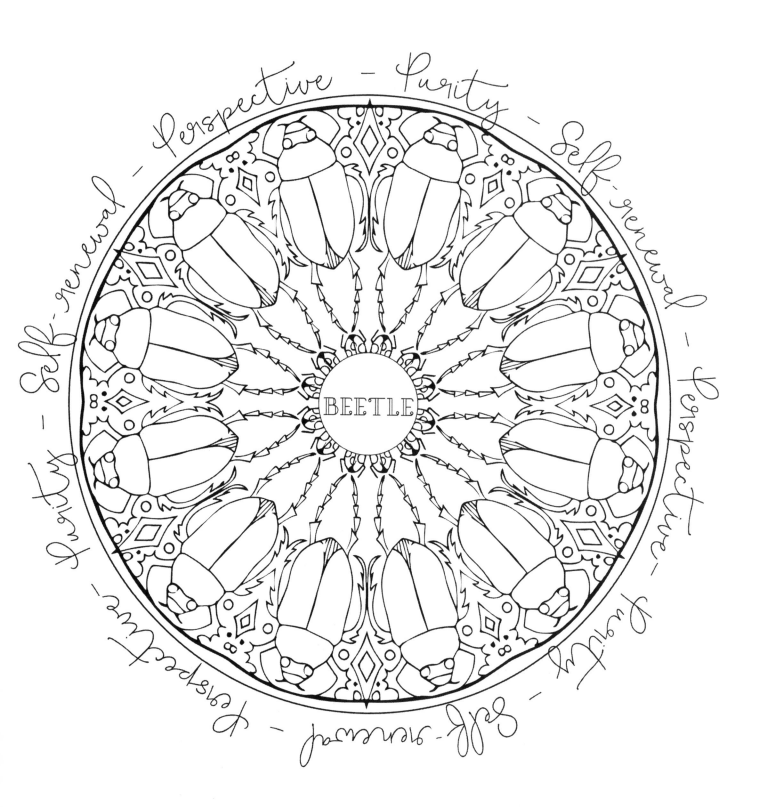

BEETLE

BOWER BIRD

selflessness

creativity

romance

BUTTER
FLY

CAMEL

celebration

endurance

innovation

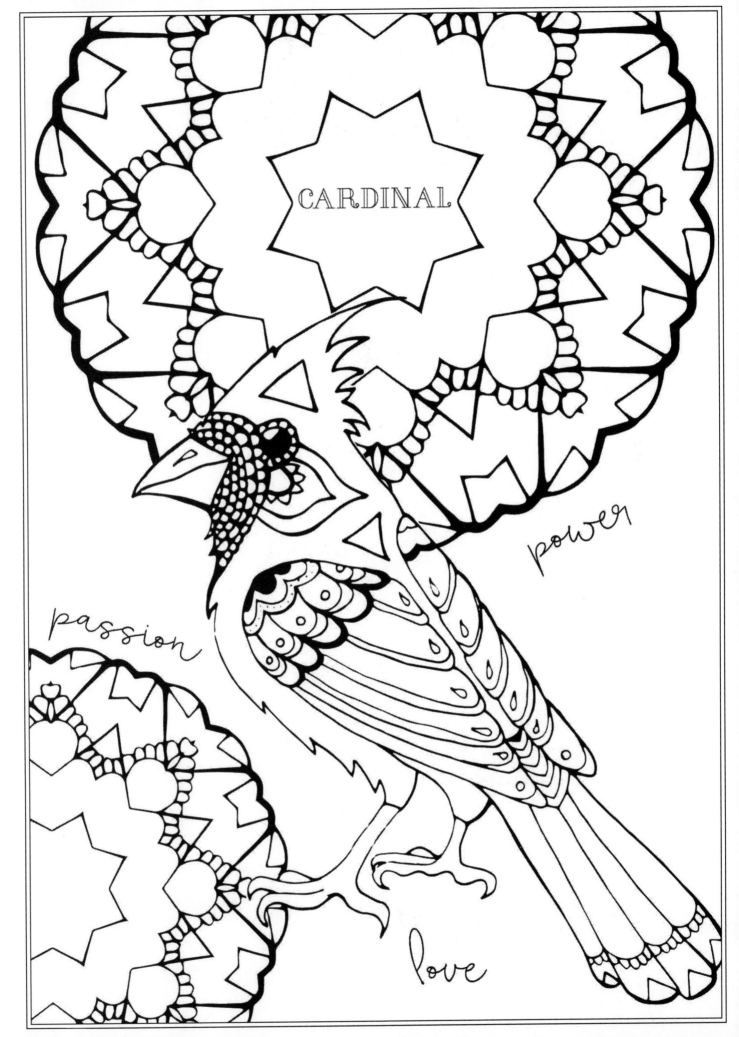

CHAMELEON

Observation – Energy – Influence – Observation – Energy – Influence – Observation – Energy – Influence – Observation – Energy – Influence

Divine Timing — Cycles — Vibration — Divine Timing — Cycles — Vibration — Divine Timing — Cycles — Vibration — Divine Timing — Cycles — Vibration — Divine Timing

CICADA

CLOWNFISH

Teamwork

Adaptation

Respect

COCKATOO

freedom

travel

creative expression

Wander   Trickster

Shapeshift   COYOTE

CRAB

cycles

trust

safety

CRICKET

Good Luck — Joy — Rebirth — Good Luck — Joy — Rebirth — Good Luck — Joy — Rebirth — Good Luck — Joy — Rebirth

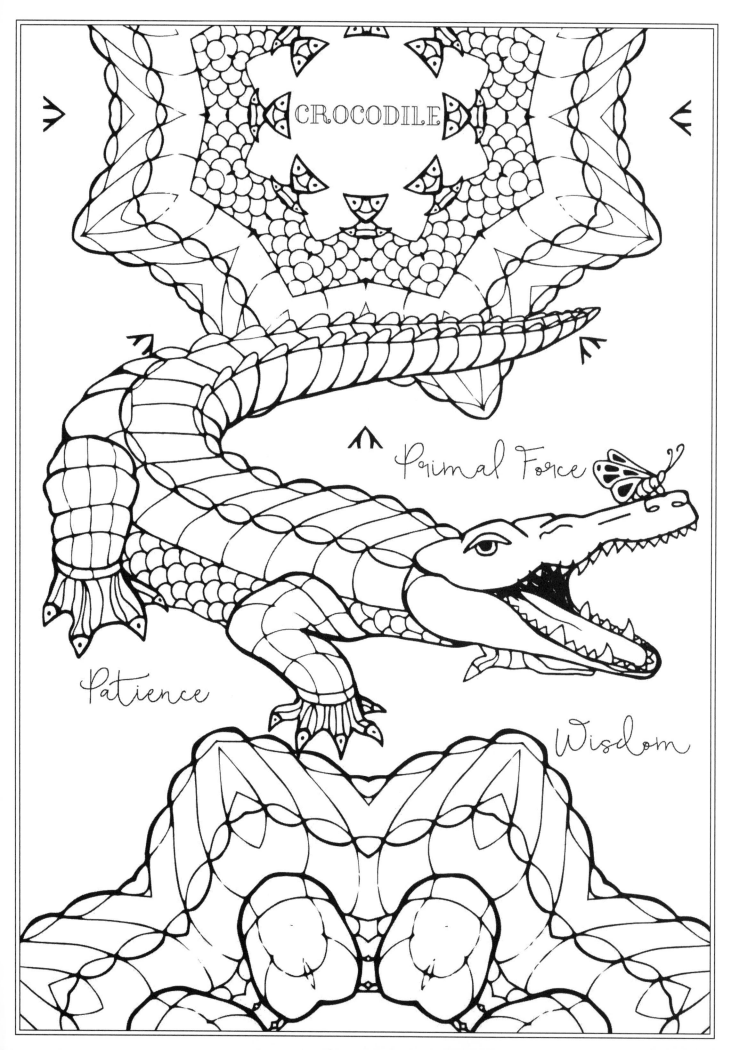

CROCODILE

Primal Force

Patience

Wisdom

DOVE

Reconciliation

Innocence

Peace

DRAGON FLY

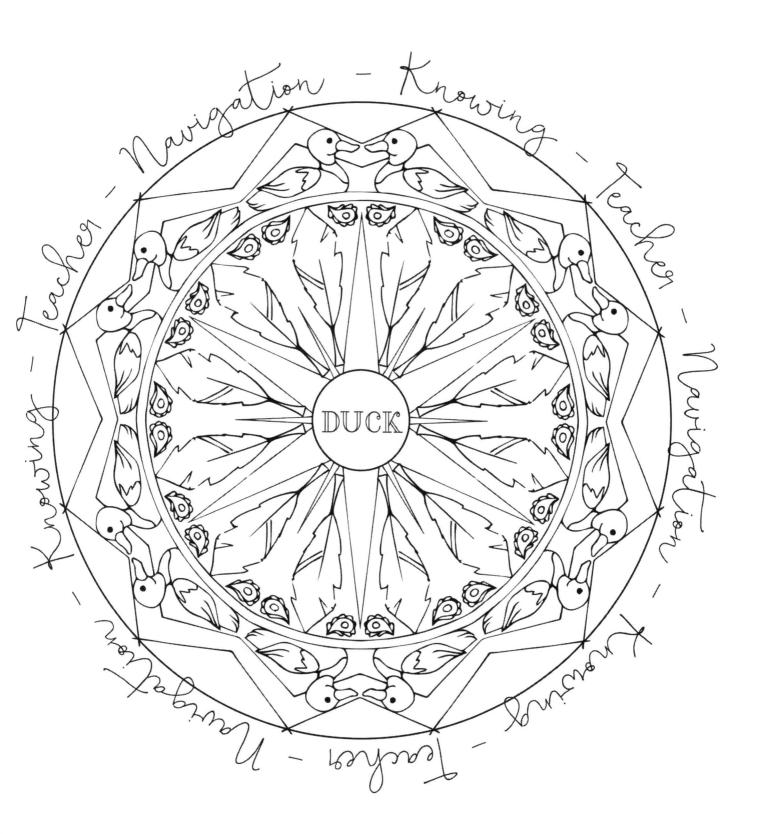

EAGLE

Strength - Resilience - Strength - Perseverance - Resilience - Resilience - Perseverance - Strength - Perseverance - Resilience - Strength

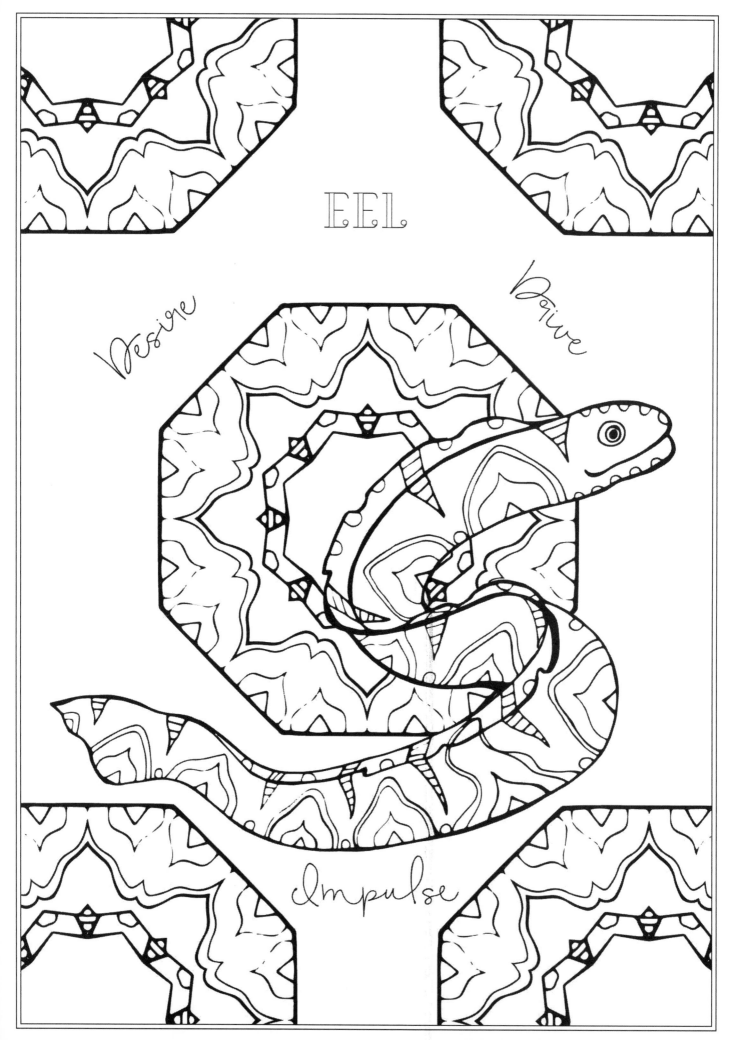

EEL

Desire

Vague

Impulse

ELEPHANT

FLAMINGO

Friendship – Community – Tradition – Friendship – Community – Tradition – Friendship – Community – Tradition – Friendship – Community – Tradition – Friendship

33

GECKO

Sensitivity – Sensuality – Sacrifice – Sensuality – Sacrifice – Sensitivity – Sensuality – Sacrifice – Sensitivity –

HAWK

Connection

Focus

Guidance

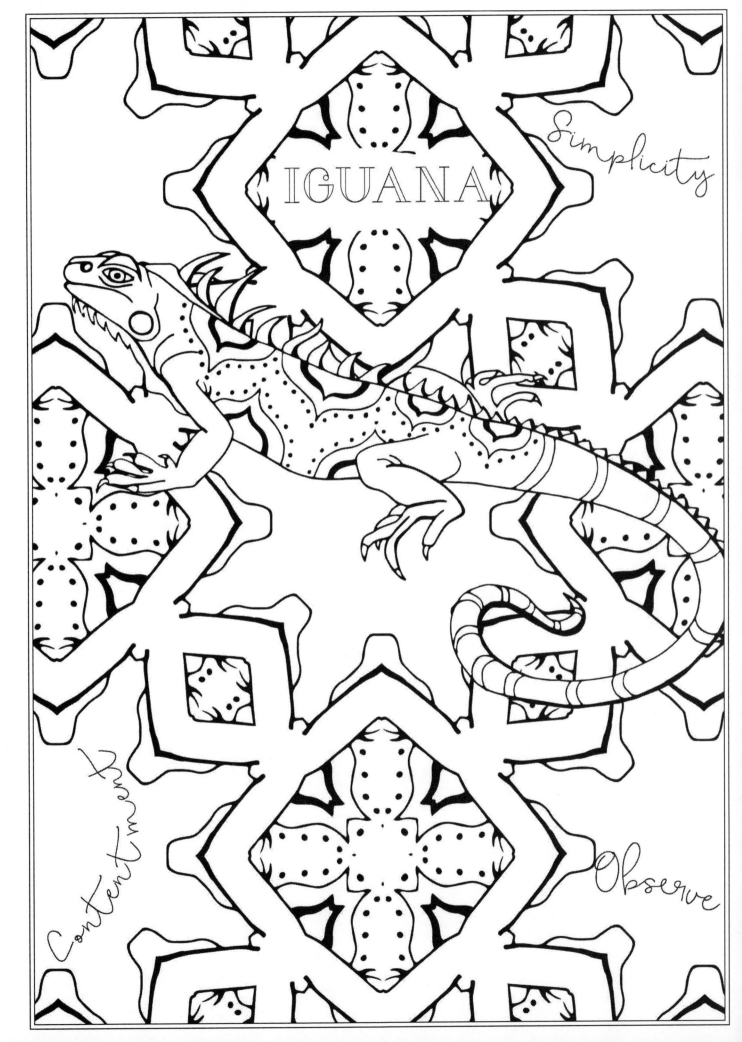

JAGUAR

Intention

Solitary

Power

Flow

Surrender

Source

JELLYFISH

KINGFISHER

Peace

Mindfulness

Trust

KOALA

Wisdom

Knowledge

Teacher

46

Perseverance

Bravery

KOI

Success

LION FISH

Action

Gifts

Emotional Strength

FRILLED NECK LIZARD

LOVEBIRDS

Love

Innocence

Partnership

MACAW

Family

Home

True Colours

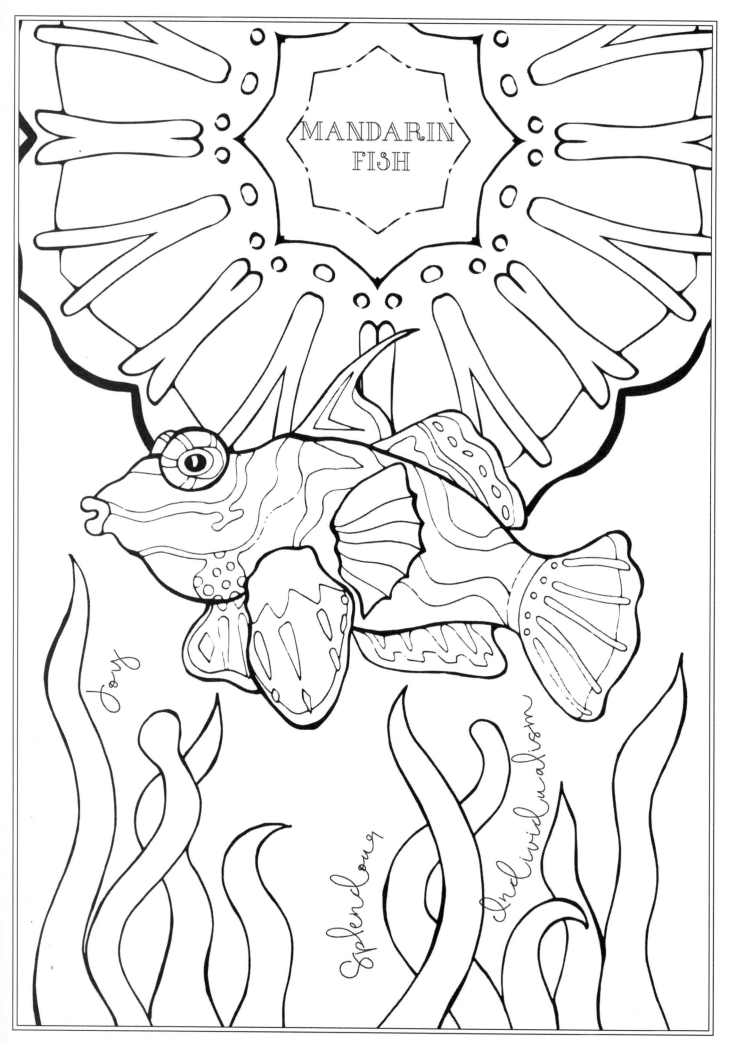

MANDARIN
FISH

MOOSE

Respect

Mindfulness

Discernment

MOTH

Knowing

Vulnerability

Awareness

ORANGUTAN

Play

Creation

Inner Child

Intuition - Wisdom - Insight - Intuition - Wisdom - Insight - Intuition - Wisdom - Insight - Strength

OWL

PARROT FISH

Authenticity - Celebration - Courage - Authenticity - Celebration - Courage - Authenticity - Celebration - Courage - Authenticity - Celebration - Courage -

PEACOCK

Inspiration – Insight – Inspiration – Passion – Insight – Insight – Passion – Inspiration – Passion – Insight – Passion – Insight

Self-discipline

Purpose

Renewal

PENGUIN

PIG

Opportunity

Abundance

Adaptability

ROOSTER

Focus

Honesty

Timekeeper

SEA
HORSE

Love – Vulnerability – Patience – Love – Vulnerability – Patience – Love – Vulnerability – Patience – Love – Vulnerability – Patience

SNAIL

Evolution

Progress

Self-reliance

SNAKE

Shedding — Life Force — Transformation — Shedding — Life Force — Transformation — Shedding — Life Force — Transformation — Shedding — Life Force

Instinct – Willpower – Courage – Instinct – Willpower – Courage – Instinct – Willpower – Courage – Instinct – Willpower – Courage

TIGER

Contentment

Treasure

TORTOISE

Longevity

TURKEY

Honour

Abundance

Gratefulness

UNICORN

WHALE SHARK

Depth

Reservation

Presence

First published and distributed in the United Kingdom by:
Hay House UK Ltd,
Astley House, 33 Notting Hill Gate, London W11 3JQ
Tel: +44 (0)20 3675 2450; Fax: +44 (0)20 3675 2451
www.hayhouse.co.uk

Published and distributed in the United Kingdom by: Hay House UK, Ltd.: www.hayhouse.co.uk • *Published and distributed in Australia by:* Hay House Australia Pty. Ltd.: www.hayhouse.com.au • *Published and distributed in the United States by:* Hay House, Inc.: www.hayhouse.com® • *Published and distributed in the Republic of South Africa by:* Hay House SA (Pty), Ltd.: www.hayhouse.co.za • *Distributed in Canada by:* Raincoast Books: www.raincoast.com • *Published in India by*: Hay House Publishers India: www.hayhouse.co.in

Cover and interior design: Sarah Wilder
Cover and interior illustrations: Nicole Brown, Niche Creative

The moral rights of the author have been asserted.

A catalogue record for this book is available from the British Library.

ISBN: 978-1-78180-832-0

Printed and bound by CPI Group (UK) Ltd, Croydon, CR0 4YY

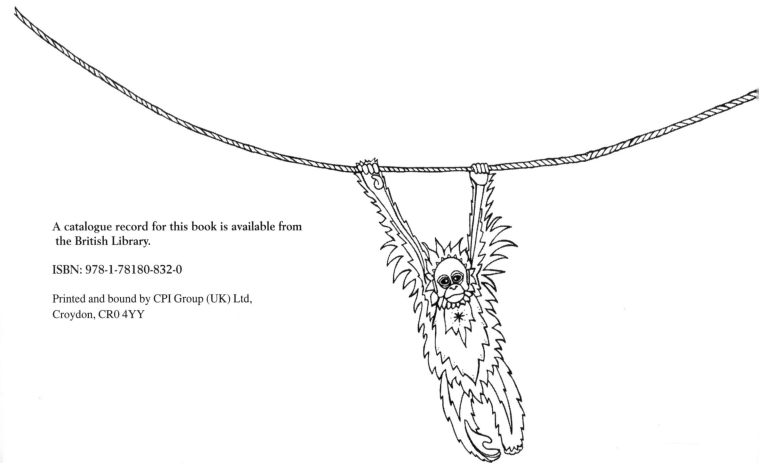